Student Workbook

D1308321

Contents

Pneumatic Test Equipment

Using Your Training Program

This is a comprehensive videotape/text training program. It may be used for independent self-study, or in a traditional classroom setting.

The videotapes are divided into segments, varying in length from four to six minutes.

This workbook is also divided into segments that generally correspond to the videotape segments.

Throughout the workbook, you will find symbols that will help you to identify how the information is organized:

Objective
Goal

Application
Doing
Hands-On

Self-Check
Review Questions
Pre/Post Test

Bibliography
Reference/Standard

Using Your Training Program

Calculator
Exercises
Computation

Concept/Idea
Understanding
Theory

Closer Look
More Information

You may alternately view a segment of videotape and read the corresponding segment in your workbook. A variety of questions and practical exercises are provided to further your understanding of the subject.

If you are undertaking your training in a classroom setting, your instructor will administer a pretest and a post test during the course. Final evaluation of your progress through the training program will be based on a combination of test scores and observation of your performance during hands-on exercises.

Student Workbook

Overview

The training program, *Pneumatic Test Equipment,* explains the characteristics and operating principles of various types of equipment used for the calibration of pneumatic instruments. In addition to information on the use of precision test gages and portable, analog- and digital-display calibrators, using deadweight testers as alternative sources of input pressures for high-pressure instruments and systems is also covered. At the end of your study of *Pneumatic Test Equipment,* you should be able to perform the training objectives of the program.

Prerequisites

Pneumatic Test Equipment is designed for individuals who have successfully completed the study of *Primary Calibration Standards* in the ITTP/2 series. In addition, it is recommended that students successfully complete the study of *Electronic Test Equipment.* An understanding of basic physics and math will also be helpful.

Test Gages

1. Define *test gage*.
2. Identify important selection factors for test gages.
3. Describe how test gages differ from general-purpose pressure gages.
4. Describe the effects of parallax.
5. Demonstrate how to minimize the effects of parallax when reading a test gage.
6. Demonstrate how to read multiple scales on test gages.
7. Demonstrate how to check the accuracy of a general-purpose pressure gage using a test gage.

Deadweight Testers

8. Demonstrate how deadweight testers are used as input pressure sources for calibration.

Analog-Display Pneumatic Calibrators

9. Define *analog-display pneumatic calibrator*.
10. Describe the parts and operating principles of analog-display pneumatic calibrators.
11. Demonstrate how to set up an analog-display pneumatic calibrator to calibrate a pneumatic instrument.
12. Demonstrate how to calibrate a pneumatic instrument using an analog-display pneumatic calibrator.

Digital-Display Pneumatic Calibrators

13. Define *digital-display pneumatic calibrator*.
14. Describe the parts and operating principles of digital-display pneumatic calibrators.
15. Demonstrate how to set up a digital-display pneumatic calibrator to calibrate a pneumatic instrument.
16. Demonstrate how to calibrate a pneumatic instrument using a digital-display pneumatic calibrator.

Test Gages

Segment 1

The purpose of test equipment is to check the accuracy of individual instruments or instrumentation and control systems. In most plants, a number of different devices or instruments are used for calibration. In a calibration, a known input that represents the value of a measured variable is applied to the instrument being tested. The output or display of the instrument should represent the value of the input. If the instrument's output does not represent the value of the input, the instrument must be adjusted until it is *in calibration*. An instrument that is in calibration produces an output that is an accurate indication of the input applied to it. Most of the test instruments used for routine calibrations are secondary standards. To ensure their accuracy, secondary standards are periodically calibrated using primary standards, such as manometers or deadweight testers.

Define test gage.

Test gages are secondary standards that are used to calibrate instruments that indicate, transmit, or record pressure. Test gages are available with a variety of ranges, including pounds per square inch (psi), inches of water (in. H_2O), vacuum, and so forth.

Identify important selection factors for test gages.

It is important to select the proper test gage for each application. Generally, it is good practice to use a gage with the smallest available range, assuming that the top of the range is greater than the highest expected pressure. Selecting a test gage that displays in the same units as the device being tested is also helpful because it eliminates the need to convert values from one scale to another.

Test gages are precision instruments. Handle them carefully. Although no external sign of damage may result, gages that are accidentally dropped or mishandled in other ways may not function properly. Test gages that have been subjected to shock through improper handling should be calibrated against a primary standard before being used to calibrate another instrument. To ensure their continued accuracy, store test gages properly.

Test Gages

Describe how test gages differ from general-purpose pressure gages.

Test gages provide a higher degree of accuracy than general-purpose gages. Consequently, the primary differences between test gages and general-purpose pressure gages are internal and cannot be readily seen. External features of test gages that are easy to identify are mirrored faces and multiple scales.

Describe the effects of parallax.

Many test gages have mirrored surfaces near the scales on their faces. A mirror helps to eliminate the effects of parallax, which can distort the accurate reading of a test gage. Parallax is an optical illusion. Formally defined, parallax is the apparent difference in spatial relations when objects in different planes are viewed from different directions. The effects of parallax cause the indication, or reading, on a gage to seem different when viewed from different angles. In reality, the gage indicator or pointer has not moved. The illusion, or parallax, is caused by the distance between the gage face and the pointer as well as by the angle from which the gage is viewed. It is possible to minimize, if not eliminate, the effect of parallax by viewing the gage directly, that is, by standing directly in front of the gage. This position ensures that the reader's eyes are at a right angle to the gage face.

Demonstrate how to minimize the effects of parallax when reading a test gage.

The mirror on a test gage helps to ensure the correct viewing position because it reflects the indicator, or pointer, if the reader's eyes are not at a right angle to the reading. If the reader's point of view is off to either the left or the right of center, the image of the pointer becomes visible in the mirror. When the reader is correctly positioned, the pointer's image cannot be seen in the mirror because the reflected image is directly behind the pointer.

Demonstrate how to read multiple scales on test gages.

Some test gages have two scales calibrated in different units. The use of multiple scales increases the range of the instrument. Some gages have a mechanism that allows the pointer to make more than one complete revolution. An example of this type of gage has two scales: one scale is read during the first revolution; the other scale is read during the second revolution. In addition, this type of gage will have a scale indicator that shows whether the pointer is on the first revolution or the second. In the example discussed in this program, the gage has two scales: one scale is calibrated in inches of water; the other is calibrated in pounds per square inch (psi). Always check the scale indicator to determine if the inner or outer part of the scale should be read. With gages with multiple scales, it is very easy to make mistakes if the reading is obtained from the wrong half of a scale.

Demonstrate how to check the accuracy of a general-purpose pressure gage using a test gage.

The equipment needed for accuracy checks on general-purpose pressure gages includes a test gage, a manifold, and an air pressure regulator. The most appropriate test gage is calibrated in the same units as the process gage and has an adequate pressure range for the pressure to be measured. Before using a test gage, make sure that its calibration is current. Facility guidelines specify how often test gages must be calibrated. If a test gage's calibration is not current, it should not be used.

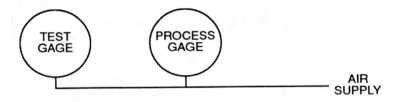

In the example discussed in this program, a test gage with a pressure scale of 0-100 pounds per square inch (psi) meets the criteria for selection. To check for accuracy, the process gage and the test gage must be connected to a regulated air supply. After the connections are made, apply the appropriate air pressure. Each gage will respond. If the process gage is accurate, the readings on both gages will be identical because the same pressure is being applied to each. If the readings differ, the process gage is not functioning properly. The gage will require adjustment and a full calibration before it can be returned to service.

It should be noted that each of the calibrations demonstrated in the shop during the course of this training program can also be done in the field. Precautions that should be taken when working in the field include the following: *Never select a test fluid without verifying that it is compatible with the process fluid associated with the instrument*

being tested. Check the supply of available test fluid before leaving the shop. Frequently, the test fluid will be instrument air. *Use care in the handling and transporting of calibration equipment.* Occasionally, the indicator, or pointer, of a test gage will stick due to hysteresis or friction in the mechanical mechanism. *Gently tap a test gage before taking a first reading to verify that the indicator mechanism is working properly.*

Hands-On Exercises

1. Become familiar with the types of test gages used in your facility. Review your facility guidelines on the calibration of test gages and the manner in which calibration dates or periods are noted.

2. Review the guidelines or procedures for using test gages to check the accuracy of pressure gages in your facility.

Review Questions

1. True or False. The primary difference between test gages and general-purpose gages is the higher degree of accuracy associated with test gages.

2. _____ is an optical illusion created by the distance between the gage face and the pointer, or indicator, and the angle at which the reading is viewed.

3. To minimize the possibility of conversion errors, test gages should be calibrated in the _____ units as those of the general-purpose gages that are being checked for accuracy or calibrated.

4. The eyes of the viewer reading a gage should be at a _____ angle to the scale in order to ensure accurate readings.

5. True or False. If a test gage has been dropped or subjected to shock in other ways, it can be reused only after the face has been carefully inspected for cracks or other visible damage.

6. When selecting a test gage, it should have the _____ available range that exceeds the highest expected pressure on the general-purpose gage being tested.

Segment 2

Pressure instruments can be calibrated quickly and accurately with test gages provided their ranges do not exceed the air pressures that are typically available. However, many instruments, including gages, have input ranges that are too high to be tested with typical air supply pressure. Deadweight testers, which are primary calibration standards, can provide the pressure source for high pressure gages and other instruments, so these testers can also be used as pressure input devices for shop calibrations.

Demonstrate how deadweight testers are used as input pressure sources for calibration.

When deadweight testers are used as pressure input devices, a manifold is connected in place of the column and piston assembly. A test gage is connected to one port of the manifold and the device to be tested is connected to the other port. The deadweight tester pump produces a pressure in the manifold. It should be noted that the deadweight tester fluid will enter the instrument being calibrated. Thus, the tester fluid must be compatible with the process in which the instrument being calibrated is installed. If the tester fluid is not compatible with the process fluids, another pressure source must be found and used. The types of fluids normally used with deadweight testers include oil, water, and alcohol. Oil-filled testers must *never* be used to calibrate instruments or devices used in oxygen systems because oil could cause explosions in the system. In oxygen applications, a pneumatic deadweight tester could be used for the calibration procedure.

After the deadweight tester has been set up, comparative readings are taken on the test gage and the instrument being tested. This step is repeated several times over the range of the instrument being tested. If the comparative readings agree at each test point, the instrument is in calibration and can be returned to service. If the readings do not agree, the instrument being tested is adjusted and the comparison tests are repeated. This process continues until the instrument readings match those of the test gage throughout the range of the instrument.

Hands-On Exercises

1. Become familiar with the types of deadweight testers used in your facility. Review your facility guidelines on the calibration of test gages using deadweight testers as input pressure devices.

2. Review the guidelines for checking the compatibility of hydraulic deadweight tester fluids and process fluids. If you have any questions, be sure to consult with your supervisor. Remember, oil-filled hydraulic testers must *never* be used to calibrate instruments installed in oxygen systems.

Review Questions

1. In addition to functioning as primary calibration standards, deadweight testers can also be used as _____ pressure sources for high pressure instrument calibrations.

2. _____ used in deadweight testers must be compatible with process systems in which the instruments being calibrated are installed.

3. A _____ directs pressure to the test gage and the instrument being tested when pressure is applied to these devices using a deadweight tester.

Segment 3

Define analog-display pneumatic calibrator.

Analog-display pneumatic calibrators are secondary standards used to calibrate pneumatic instruments. This type of calibrator allows the direct comparison of an instrument's input and output signals under test conditions. Most pneumatic calibrators are portable, which eliminates the need to remove instruments and take them back to the shop, and makes them ideal for field checks and calibrations.

Describe the parts and operating principles of analog-display pneumatic calibrators.

The components of a calibrator include a precision pressure gage, a selector valve, and two precision pressure regulators that are mounted on a panel. An air filter is located beneath the panel. A connection block provides the means for connections to an air supply and to the instrument being calibrated.

Demonstrate how to set up an analog-display pneumatic calibrator to calibrate a pneumatic instrument.

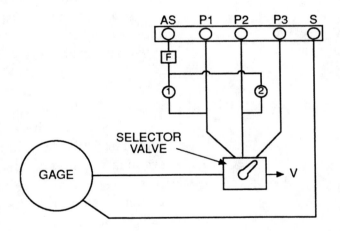

Several ports are needed to make the connections necessary to do a calibration. *Port AS* is the air supply port for the calibrator. Most analog-display pneumatic calibrators are rated for a maximum output of 30 psig. When the air supply is connected to the port, air flows through the air filter and is supplied to the inputs of the two precision pressure regulators. Pressure supplied by *Regulator 1* flows to *Port P1*, and the instrument connected to it. Port P1 is also connected to an input port of the *selector valve*. Similarly, *Regulator 2* supplies air to *Port P2* and to an input port to the selector valve. During calibration, Port P1 or Port P2 or both supply input pressures to the instrument being calibrated. There are usually at least three port positions indicated on the selector valve. The valve is positioned to select the source of the pressure signal (Port 1, Port 2, or Port 3) that will be applied to the sensing element of the instrument being calibrated.

Another port, usually identified as a *Vent Port*, allows venting of the pressure-sensing element of the instrument and the gage. *Port S* is connected directly to the case of the precision pressure gage. If an absolute pressure instrument was being calibrated, a vacuum would be connected to Port S.

Demonstrate how to calibrate a pneumatic instrument using an analog-display pneumatic calibrator.

Assume that the instrument being calibrated is a pneumatic transmitter. The transmitter is rated for an input pressure of 0-250 inches of water (in. H_2O). The output of the transmitter is a 3-15 psi air pressure signal that is proportional to the input pressure. In order to calibrate the instrument, a known pressure must be applied to its input and its output pressure must be measured. Both functions can be performed by an analog-display pneumatic calibrator.

The calibrator selected must have a range suitable for the application. In the example provided, the calibrator's range is -3.6 to 30.6 psig. It is understood that calibrators are subject to the same restrictions as other secondary standards. Periodically, secondary standards such as calibrators must be calibrated to a primary standard, such as a deadweight tester or a manometer. Under no circumstances should a calibrator with an outdated calibration be used.

In preparation for a calibration, precision gages should be *exercised* to minimize the effect of hysteresis. *To exercise a gage, cap off the appropriate port for the calibrator being used.* For this model, the cap is placed on Port P1. *Connect a regulated air supply to the calibrator. Adjust the pressure to the calibrator's supply pressure rating, then open the isolation valve. Using the selector valve, select the appropriate port.* In this example, it is Port P1. *Increase the pressure on the appropriate regulator for the port to the highest value on the gage face.* Regulator 1 supplies air to Port P1, so it is the regulator for this application.

Hold the pressure briefly, then vent back to zero. Repeat these steps once again to complete the process, as it must be done twice. Since many process fluids are hazardous or toxic, instruments must be cleaned and decontaminated according to facility guidelines or procedures before any work, such as calibration, is done on them.

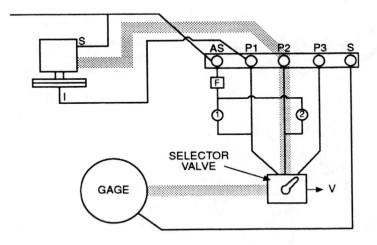

To set up the calibration, connect an air supply to the transmitter and the calibrator. The air supply to the calibrator provides the pressure for the test signals required for the calibration. *Connect the input port and the output port of the instrument being tested to the appropriate ports on the calibrator.* These ports will be specified in the operating instructions. In the example, the technician connects the transmitter's input port to Port P1. The transmitter's output is connected to Port P3. The calibrator precision gage indicates the input pressures and output pressures of the transmitter during the calibration.

The regulators receive supply air pressure through a filter and regulate the output, applying known pressures to the instrument being tested. In this example, Regulator 1 supplies a test pressure signal through Port P1 to the transmitter's input. Positioning the selector valve to Port P1 displays the input pressure reading on the gage. To obtain a display of the transmitter's output, the valve is positioned to Port P3 and the reading appears on the gage.

To begin the calibration, position the selector valve to the appropriate port and adjust the corresponding regulator to the required pressure. In the example discussed in this program, Port P1 and Regulator 1 are selected. The technician applies a pressure of 125 in. H_2O to the transmitter input. *Position the selector valve to the Vent Port to depressurize the sensor and gage. Then, reposition the selector valve to display the transmitter's output on the calibrator precision gage.* To see the output reading, the selector valve is positioned to Port P3. The reading displayed on the gage is 10.8 psi.

During calibration, repeat these steps as many times as necessary and record the readings taken at the appropriate pressures to ensure a complete calibration check throughout the range of the transmitter. The input and output values for each test point are compared with the specifications for the instrument being calibrated. If the values meet the calibration values for the instrument, no further action is required. Otherwise, adjustments are made as necessary and calibration checks are repeated.

In order to calibrate an absolute pressure gage, a vacuum pump is required. *To measure absolute pressure, connect a vacuum pump to the appropriate port on the calibrator.* In the instrument used as an example, Port S provides a direct connection to the gage case. *Evacuate the gage case and verify that the gage pointer is indicating a vacuum.* The gage pointer will indicate a pressure below atmosphere (vacuum) when the case has been evacuated. *Connect the pressure to be measured to the appropriate port.* For this instrument, the gage input is connected to Port 3. *Position the selector valve to display the absolute pressure value, and record the data point.* These steps are repeated as necessary to ensure a full check of the instrument's range.

Hands-On Exercises

1. Become familiar with the analog-display pneumatic calibrators used in your facility. Review the manufacturers' instructions and facility guidelines governing their use in the field and in the shop.

2. Review your facility's guidelines on cleaning and decontaminating process instruments before working on them or calibrating them. Be sure to follow manufacturers' instructions when working on any process instruments.

Review Questions

1. True or False. Analog-display calibrators require unit-to-unit conversions in order to compare an instrument's input and output signals under test conditions.

2. Because most pneumatic calibrators are _____ , they can be used for field checks and calibration of instruments in their normal operating locations.

3. The pressure supplied by _____ is channeled to various ports as well as to the selector valve, which directs the pressure signal to the pressure-sensing element of the instrument being calibrated.

4. Increasing the pressure on the instrument being calibrated from zero value pressure to the highest value on the gage face, holding it briefly at that value, then venting back to zero is the first step in a two-step process to eliminate _____.

5. True or False. Before work is done on any instrument, it should be cleaned and decontaminated owing to the hazardous or toxic process fluids to which it may be exposed.

Segment 4

Define digital-display pneumatic calibrator.

The function of digital-display pneumatic calibrators is identical to that of pneumatic calibrators that provide analog displays. Digital-display pneumatic calibrators are secondary standards that can be used to calibrate pneumatic instruments. Both types of calibrators allow direct comparison of an instrument's input and output signals under test conditions. However, digital-display models differ from analog-display models in construction and operation.

The most notable difference between these types of calibrators stems from the way in which each type measures and displays pressures. On digital-display pneumatic calibrators, pressures are measured and displayed electronically instead of by precision pressure gages. It should be noted that digital-display calibrators are neither more nor less accurate than analog-display calibrators. However, digital measurements tend to be read more accurately because they are easier to read than the indications provided on analog scales.

Describe the parts and operating principles of digital-display pneumatic calibrators.

Some digital-display calibrators measure pressure with an optical pressure sensor. An optical pressure sensor converts pressure inputs to equivalent electrical signals. Gage pressures, absolute pressures, differential pressures, and vacuum pressures can all be measured by this type of sensor.

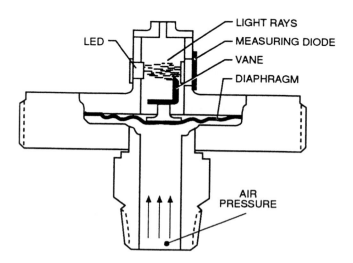

The pressure or pressures to be measured are applied to a diaphragm. As changes in pressure cause the diaphragm to move, the diaphragm changes the position of a vane. The optical pressure sensor assembly generates a signal proportional to the pressure on the diaphragm. A light-emitting diode (LED) is located at the top of the sensor housing. A measuring diode on the other side of the housing generates a signal proportional to the amount of light that the diode receives. Pressure positions the diaphragm and vane, which varies the amount of light received by the measuring diode, which, in turn, determines its output. Therefore, the output of the measuring diode is proportional to the pressure on the diaphragm. The pressure represented by the output of the measuring diode is displayed digitally on the calibrator panel.

In addition to the optical sensor and the display panel, the components of a digital-display pneumatic calibrator include a unit selection push button used to select the pressure units to be displayed and an electric power supply that usually includes internal rechargeable batteries. (Some models may require an external source of power.) As with analog models, digital units also have precision air pressure regulators, a selector valve, and connections for pneumatic inputs and outputs.

Demonstrate how to set up a digital-display pneumatic calibrator to calibrate a pneumatic instrument.

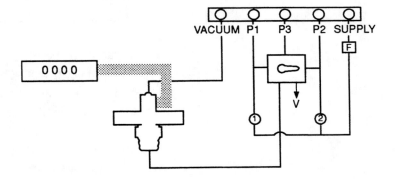

This illustration represents the internal connections of the calibrator. To provide an input to the two regulators, an air supply is connected to the *Supply Port*. *Regulator 1* supplies pressure to *Port 1*. *Regulator 2* supplies pressure to *Port 2*. *Port 3* is connected to the selector valve, but it should be noted that in this model *Port 3* is not connected to a pressure regulator. The position of the selector valve determines the port from which the pressure signal is applied. The pressure signal from the selected port is directed to and measured by the diaphragm pressure sensor. The *Vent Port* is used to depressurize the sensor. The *Vacuum Port* is connected above the pressure sensor diaphragm. For absolute pressure measurements, a vacuum source is connected to the Vacuum Port. The output of the measuring diode is electrically connected to the digital display on the calibrator panel.

Demonstrate how to calibrate a pneumatic instrument using a digital-display pneumatic calibrator.

The pneumatic instrument used as an example in this program is a pneumatic differential pressure transmitter. The transmitter is connected or installed as a level transmitter on a tank. For this application, the transmitter has a filled reference leg.

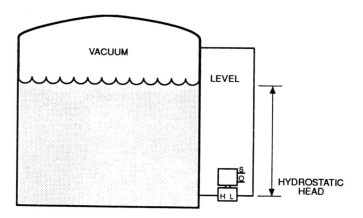

As indicated in the illustration, the high-side port of the transmitter is connected to the bottom of the tank. The transmitter's low side port is connected to the bottom of a liquid-filled reference leg. The reference leg is connected at the top of the tank in the vapor space. Therefore, the pressure on the low-side port of the transmitter is a combination of the hydrostatic head of the liquid in the reference leg and the vapor pressure in the tank. The output pressure of the transmitter is the difference between two measured pressures: the hydrostatic head, or height, of the liquid in the tank and the pressure in the reference leg.

In order to calibrate the transmitter, a constant pressure signal must be supplied to the low-side port of the transmitter to compensate for the hydrostatic head produced by the liquid in the reference leg. The signal supplied to the high-side port of the transmitter will be varied and compared to the transmitter's output. The transmitter used as an example has a rated input of 0-100 inches of water differential pressure (0-100 in. H_2O dP). It transmits a corresponding air pressure output of 3-15 psi.

Preparations for using digital-display pneumatic calibrators are very similar to those required for analog models: *Exercise the calibrator's pressure sensor to minimize the effects of hysteresis. Check the settings of the regulators to be certain they are at the lowest possible settings. Connect the supply air to the calibrator and to the instrument being calibrated.* Internal connections between the instrument and the calibrator are dictated by the requirements of each application.

In this application, the calibrator is furnishing the input test pressure, so the high-side input of the transmitter is connected to Port P1 on the calibrator. This makes it possible to vary the signal from Regulator 1 to simulate changes in the level of the tank. The low-side input of the transmitter is connected to Port P2 on the calibrator. Regulator 2 then provides a pressure that is equal to the hydrostatic head of the reference leg. The output of the transmitter is connected to Port P3, so that the transmitter's output signal can be measured, displayed, and monitored during the calibration. The proper positioning of the selector valve makes it possible to see the transmitter's high-side input pressures, low-side input pressures, and output pressures on the digital display.

To begin the calibration, place the selector valve in the appropriate position. For this example, the selector valve is placed in the Port 2 Position. *Adjust the regulator to apply the appropriate pressure value.* Regulator 2 is adjusted to apply a pressure of 100 in. H_2O to the transmitter's low side input. This pressure value is equal to the hydrostatic head of the reference column. For the calibrator used in this application, the selector valve is positioned to Port P3 in order to read the output of the transmitter. With reference leg pressure applied to the low-side input and no pressure value applied to the high-side input, the output of the transmitter should be equivalent to zero level in the tank. Given the transmitter's output range of 3-15 psi, the output of the transmitter should be 3 psi.

Digital-Display Pneumatic Calibrators

Before proceeding to the next test point, vent the pressure sensor. Reposition the selector valve for the next appropriate position. In this application, the selector valve is placed in the Port P1 position. *Adjust the regulator to apply the appropriate pressure value.* Regulator 1 is used to apply the appropriate pressure value to the transmitter's high-side input. *Reposition the selector valve to display the reading. Record the data point.* The process is repeated for several values throughout the range of the transmitter and input and output readings are noted for each value. *Compare the input and output data for each test point with the calibration standards established for the instrument to determine if adjustments are required.* The instrument is in calibration if the data for each test point is within the transmitter specifications.

Hands-On Exercises

1. Become familiar with the digital-display pneumatic calibrators used in your facility. Review the manufacturers' instructions and facility guidelines governing their use in the field and in the shop.

2. Review the calibration schedule for the instruments in a process system with which you are familiar. Compare the calibration guidelines for the various instruments in the process, and identify any significant differences among them. If you are not sure why some procedures differ from others, ask your supervisor for an explanation. Remember to always follow manufacturers' instructions when working on any process instruments.

Review Questions

1. Due to the electronic circuits used to display measurements, _____ pneumatic calibrators require a power source.

2. True or False. Only analog-display pneumatic calibrators need to be exercised to minimize the effects of hysteresis.

3. During a calibration, the pressure sensor must be _____ after each pressure value has been applied.

4. While setting up the unit for a calibration, the regulators on a calibrator should be checked to determine that they are at their _____ setting.

5. True or False. Digital-display pneumatic calibrators are more accurate than analog-display units.

Answer Key

Review Questions — Test Gages

1. True. The primary difference between test gages and general-purpose gages is the higher degree of accuracy associated with test gages.

2. Parallax is an optical illusion created by the distance between the gage face and the pointer, or indicator, and the angle at which the reading is viewed.

3. To minimize the possibility of conversion errors, test gages should be calibrated in the same units as those of the general-purpose gages that are being checked for accuracy or calibrated.

4. The eyes of the viewer reading a gage should be at a right angle to the scale in order to ensure accurate readings.

5. False. If a test gage has been dropped or subjected to shock in other ways, it can be returned to service only after it has been recalibrated.

6. When selecting a test gage, it should have the smallest available range that exceeds the highest expected pressure on the general-purpose gage being tested.

Review Questions — Deadweight Testers

1. In addition to functioning as primary calibration standards, deadweight testers can also be used as input pressure sources for high pressure instrument calibrations.

2. Fluids used in deadweight testers must be compatible with process systems in which the instruments being calibrated are installed.

3. A manifold directs pressure to the test gage and the instrument being tested when pressure is applied to these devices using a deadweight tester.

Review Questions — Analog-Display Pneumatic Calibrators

1. False. Analog-display calibrators allow direct comparison of an instrument's input and output signals under test conditions.

2. Because most pneumatic instruments are portable, they can be used for field checks and calibration of instruments in their normal operating locations.

3. The pressure supplied by regulators is channeled to various ports as well as to the selector valve, which directs the pressure signal to the pressure-sensing element of the instrument being calibrated.

4. Increasing the pressure on the instrument being calibrated from zero value pressure to the highest value on the gage face, holding it briefly at that value, then venting back to zero is the first step in a two-step process to eliminate hysteresis.

5. True. Before work is done on any instrument, it should be cleaned and decontaminated owing to the hazardous or toxic process fluids to which it may be exposed.

Review Questions — Digital-Display Pneumatic Calibrators

1. Due to the electronic circuits used to display measurements, digital-display pneumatic calibrators require a power source.

2. False. Before beginning calibration procedures, the mechanical mechanisms of all types of precision instruments should be exercised to minimize the effects of hysteresis.

3. During a calibration, the pressure sensor must be vented after each pressure value has been applied.

4. While setting up the unit for a calibration, the regulators on a calibrator should be checked to determine that they are at their lowest setting.

5. False. Digital-display pneumatic calibrators are neither more nor less accurate than analog-display units.

Glossary

Absolute pressure	1. The combined local pressure induced by some source and the atmospheric pressure at the location of the measurement. 2. Gage pressure plus barometric pressure in the same units.
Accuracy	In process instrumentation, degree of conformity of an indicated value to a recognized accepted standard value or ideal value.
Analog	The representation of numerical quantities by means of physical variables, such as translation, rotation, voltage, or resistance; contrasted with digital. A waveform is analog if it is continuous and varies over an arbitrary range.
Analog data	Data represented in a continuous form, as contrasted with digital data represented in a discrete, discontinuous form. Analog data are usually represented by means of physical variables, such as voltage, resistance, rotation, and so forth.
Calibration	Determination of the experimental relationship between the quantity being measured and the output of the device that measures it; where the quantity measured is obtained through a recognized standard of measurement.
Deadweight gage	A device used to generate accurate pressures for the purpose of calibrating pressure gages; freely balanced weights (dead weights) are loaded on a calibrated piston to give a static hydraulic pressure output.
Decade	A group or assembly of ten units, e.g., a counter that counts to ten in one column, or a resistor box that inserts resistance quantities in multiple powers of 10.
Differential-pressure transmitter	Any of several transducers designed to measure the difference in pressure between two enclosed spaces, independent of their absolute pressures.
Digital	1. Pertaining to data in the form of digits. Contrast with analog. 2. A method of measurement using precise quantities to measure variables.
Digital data	Data represented in discrete discontinuous form, as contrasted with analog data represented in continuous form. Digital data is usually represented by means of coded characters, for example, numbers, signs, symbols, and so forth.
Diode	A two-electrode electronic component containing merely an anode and a cathode.

Glossary

Hysteresis	1. A phenomenon demonstrated by materials that make their behavior a function of the history of the environment to which they have been subjected. Hysteresis is usually determined by subtracting the value of dead band from the maximum measured separation between upscale-going and downscale-going indications of the measured variable (during a full range traverse, unless otherwise specified) after transients have decayed. This measurement is sometimes called hysteresis error or hysteretic error. Some reversal of output may be expected for any reversal of input; this distinguishes hysteresis from dead band. 2. The tendency of an instrument to give a different output for a given input, depending on whether the input resulted from an increase or decrease from the previous value.
Inclined-tube manometer	A glass-tube manometer having one leg inclined from the vertical to give more precise readings.
Light-emitting diode (LED)	A semiconductor diode that emits visible or infrared light. Light from an LED is incoherent spontaneous emission, as distinct from the coherent stimulated emission produced by diode lasers and other types of lasers.
Manometer	A gage for measuring pressure or a pressure difference between two fluid chambers. A U-tube manometer consists of two legs, each containing a specific known gravity.
Meniscus	The concave or convex surface caused by surface tension at the top of a liquid column, as in a manometer tube.
NIST	National Institute of Standards and Technology, U.S. Department of Commerce (formerly, National Bureau of Standards).
Optical pressure transducer	Any of several devices that use optical methods to accurately measure the position of the sensitive element of the pressure transducer.
Parallax	The apparent difference in spatial relations when objects in different planes are viewed from different directions; in making instrument readings, for instance, parallax will cause an error in the observed value unless the observer's eye is directly in line with the pointer.
Primary instrument	An instrument that can be calibrated without reference to another instrument.

Glossary

Range	1. For instrumentation, the set of values over which measurements can be made without changing the instrument's sensitivity. 2. The extent of a measuring, indicating, or recording scale. 3. The set of values that a quantity or function may assume. 4. The difference between the highest and lowest value that a quantity or function may assume.
Standard gage	A highly accurate gage used only as a reference standard for checking or calibrating working gages.
Test gage	A pressure gage specially built for test service or other types of work that require a high degree of accuracy and repeatability.
Transducer	Any device or component that converts an input signal of one form to an output signal of another form — for instance, a piezoelectric transducer converts pressure waves into electrical signals, or vice versa.
Vacuum	A low-pressure gaseous environment having an absolute pressure lower than ambient atmospheric pressure.
Well-type manometer	A type of double-leg glass-tube manometer in which one leg is substantially smaller than the other; the large-diameter leg acts as a reservoir whose liquid level does not change appreciably with changes in pressure.

ISA Publications

Application Concepts of Process Control. P. W. Murrill. Instrument Society of America, Research Triangle Park, NC. 1988. (ISBN: 1-55617-171-4)

Automatic Tuning of PID Controllers. K. J. Astrom and T. Hagglund. Instrument Society of America, Research Triangle Park, NC. 1988. (ISBN: 1-55617-081-5)

Electronic Controllers. L. M. Thompson. Instrument Society of America, Research Triangle Park, NC. 1989. (ISBN: 1-555617-129-3)

Flow Measurement. D. W. Spitzer, ed. Instrument Society of America, Research Triangle Park, NC. 1991. (ISBN: 1-555617-334-2)

Fundamentals of Flow Measurement. J. P. DeCarlo. Instrument Society of America, Research Triangle Park, NC. 1984. (ISBN: 0-087664-627-5)

Fundamentals of Process Control Theory., 2nd ed. P. W. Murrill. Instrument Society of America, Research Triangle Park, NC. 1981. (ISBN: 0-87664-507-4)

Industrial Flow Measurement, 2nd ed. D. W. Spitzer. Instrument Society of America, Research Triangle Park, NC. 1990. (ISBN: 1-555617-243-5)

Industrial Pressure Measurement. D. R. Gillum. Instrument Society of America, Research Triangle Park, NC. 1982. (ISBN: 0-87664-668-2)

Measurement and Control of Liquid Level. C. H. Cho. Instrument Society of America, Research Triangle Park, NC. 1982. (ISBN: 0-87664-625-9)

Process Control Fundamentals Package. Instrument Society of America, Research Triangle Park, NC. 1987. (ISBN: 1-55617-195-1)

Bibliography

INVOLVE ®
Interactive
Videodisc Instruction

Bibliography

Industrial Measurement Series. Instrument Society of America, Research Triangle Park, NC. 1987.

Controller Tuning Series
Instrument Society of America, Research Triangle Park, NC. 1990.

Electronic Maintenance Series
Instrument Society of America, Research Triangle Park, NC. 1991.

Industrial Process Control Series
Instrument Society of America, Research Triangle Park, NC. 1991.

Interpreting Process Control Diagrams
Instrument Society of America, Research Triangle Park, NC. 1990.

Troubleshooting Series
Instrument Society of America, Research Triangle Park, NC. 1990.

Index

A

Absolute pressure   12, 16
Air filter   9, 11
Analog display   12, 14
Analog-display pneumatic
    calibrator   9

C

Calibration   3, 5, 12, 17, 18

D

Deadweight tester   7
Diaphragm   14
Diaphragm pressure sensor   16
Differential pressure   17
Digital display   14
Digital-display pneumatic
    calibrator   14

E

Electric power supply   15

F

Field checks   9

H

Hydrostatic head   16, 17
Hysteresis   10, 17

I

Input pressures   11, 17
Input values   12
Instrument air   6

L

Light-emitting diode (LED)   15

M

Measuring diode   15

O

Optical pressure sensor   14
Output pressures   11, 17
Output values   12

P

Parallax   4
Port positions   10
Ports   9, 10, 15
Pressure regulators
    9, 10, 11, 15
Pressure signal   10
Primary standard   3, 10
Process fluids   11

R

Range   10
Reference leg   16

S

Secondary standard
    3, 10, 14
Selector valve   9, 10, 11, 15
Sensing element   10
Sensor   12

T

Test equipment   3
Test fluid   6
Test gage   3, 4
Test signals   11

V

Vacuum   12
Vacuum pump   12
Vane   15
Vapor pressure   16